# DK READERS

LEARNING TO READ
pre-level 1

# STAR WARS

# Blast Off!

Get ready to meet
some exciting people
and creatures.

5... 4... 3... 2... 1...
Blast off!

Meet Anakin Skywalker.
He is a Jedi Knight.

**lightsaber**

Anakin

Meet R2-D2.

He is a droid.

He can fix other droids.

R2-D2

Meet C-3PO.
He is a droid.
He can speak many
languages.

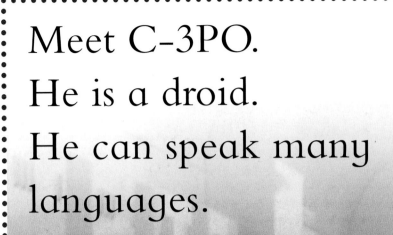

C-3PO

Padmé

Meet Padmé Amidala.
She is a Senator.

Obi-Wan

Meet Obi-Wan
Kenobi. He is a
Jedi Master.

**beard**

Meet Yoda. He is the
most powerful Jedi.

Yoda

**walking
stick**

Meet Jar Jar Binks.
He is very clumsy.

ears

Jar Jar Binks

# Meet Luke Skywalker.
## He is a good pilot.

cape

Luke

Meet Leia Organa.
She is a Princess.

**uniform**

Leia

**blaster**

Han

Meet Han Solo.

He is a pilot.

He flies a fast ship.

# Meet Chewbacca.
# He is a brave co-pilot.

fur

Chewbacca

# Darth Vader

# Meet Darth Vader.
# He is a powerful villain.

**helmet**

# Now you have met everyone.

# Who is your favourite?

# Glossary

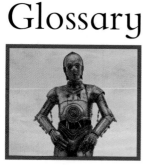

**Droid**
another word for a robot

**Jedi**
a person who can use the Force

**Lightsaber**
a special sword with a blade made of light

**Senator**
a member of the galactic government

**Villain**
a bad person